W9-AWL-770

Timeless Tales from PANCHATANTRA

An imprint of Om Books International

Om KIDZ | Om Books International

Reprinted in 2020

Corporate & Editorial Office
A-12, Sector 64, Noida 201 301
Uttar Pradesh, India
Phone: +91 120 477 4100
Email: editorial@ombooks.com
Website: www.ombooksinternational.com

Sales Office
107, Ansari Road, Darya Ganj
New Delhi 110 002, India
Phone: +91 11 4000 9000
Email: sales@ombooks.com
Website: www.ombooks.com

ISBN: 978-93-80070-35-3

Printed in India

10

Contents

The Mice and the Elephants

Once upon a time, there lived a group of mice under a big tree in a forest. There were thousands of mice in that group. They used to live happily together and were headed by

King Mouse. The king was very kind and helpful to others. He would tell his fellow mice to always be kind.

One day, a big group of elephants came near the tree. They were searching for water as they were thirsty and tired. In this condition, they did not notice the mice living under the tree and destroyed their homes by accident. Some of the mice were also crushed under their feet and wounded. The others started running here and there.

They pleaded to their king, "Oh wise king, save us from these mad elephants, otherwise they will destroy our homes. They will kill all of us!" The king assured his fellow mice, "Do not worry my dear friends, nothing will happen."

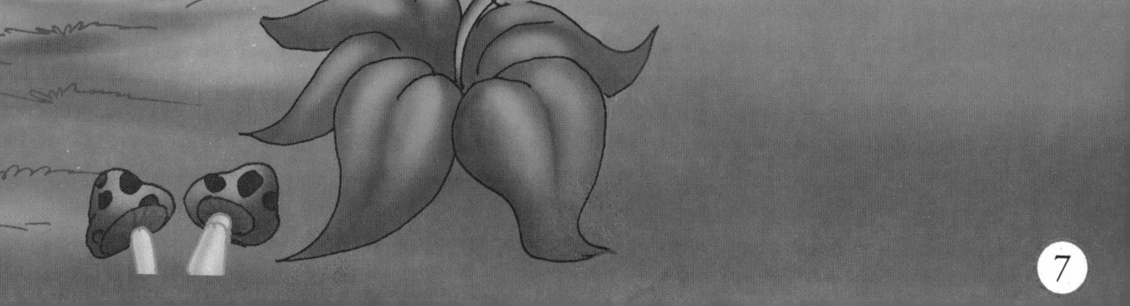

He then approached the chief of the elephants' group. Instead of showing anger, he politely requested the mighty chief, "Sir, kindly guide your group from some other route and spare our homes and lives."

The chief of elephants was kind and he understood the plight of the little mice. He said, "I am really sorry, my dear friend. We did not notice your group living here. We were thirsty and looking for water."

The king of mice told him about a route where they could find water. The elephants apologised to the mice and moved towards the other route.

The king of mice said, "Look friends! We are saved and we learnt a lesson today that with kind words, we can win over any bad situation."

One day, some elephant-hunters came to the forest and trapped all the elephants in huge nets. The elephants had lost all hope of escaping and thought that nobody could save their lives now.

The chief of elephants suddenly thought of the group of mice; they would be able to chew through these nets! Since he was trapped in the net, the chief called out to a bird who was flying past.

He asked the bird to approach the king of mice and tell him about the situation. The bird quickly flew to the big tree and told the king of mice about the danger that the elephants faced.

The king of mice said to all the mice, "We should all go and help them, for they were kind to us."

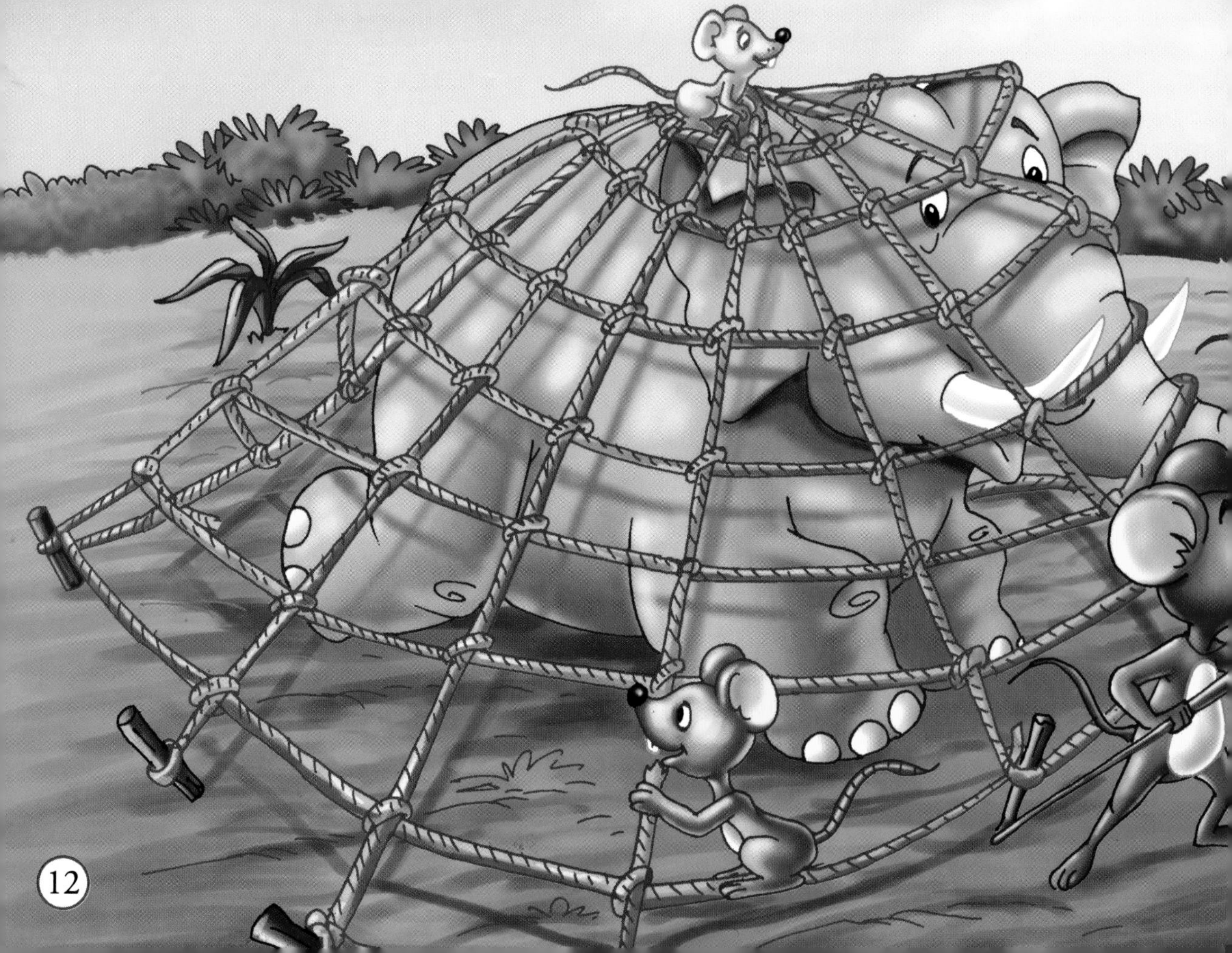

Within a few minutes, thousands of mice reached there and chewed through all the nets with the help of their sharp teeth, and set the elephants free.

The elephants thanked the mice again and again, and from that day onwards, they all lived happily together in the forest.

The Horse and the Lion

Once upon a time, there was a farmer who had a horse. Now, the poor horse had become very old and sick, and so the farmer thought that the old horse was of no use to him. He started treating the horse as a burden.

Finally, the farmer asked the horse to leave his house and to go and live in the forest. The horse became very sad and started crying. He thought, "Now, when I am old and needy, my master is treating me badly."

He said to his master, "Master, I have always been your faithful servant. I have worked hard day after day for many years. How can you ask me to leave the house at this age? Is this the reward I am getting for my loyalty and labour?"

On hearing this, the farmer had no answer so he kept a condition to keep the horse at home. He said, "Alright, you can live in my house, provided you bring me a lion. I want a lion's skin."

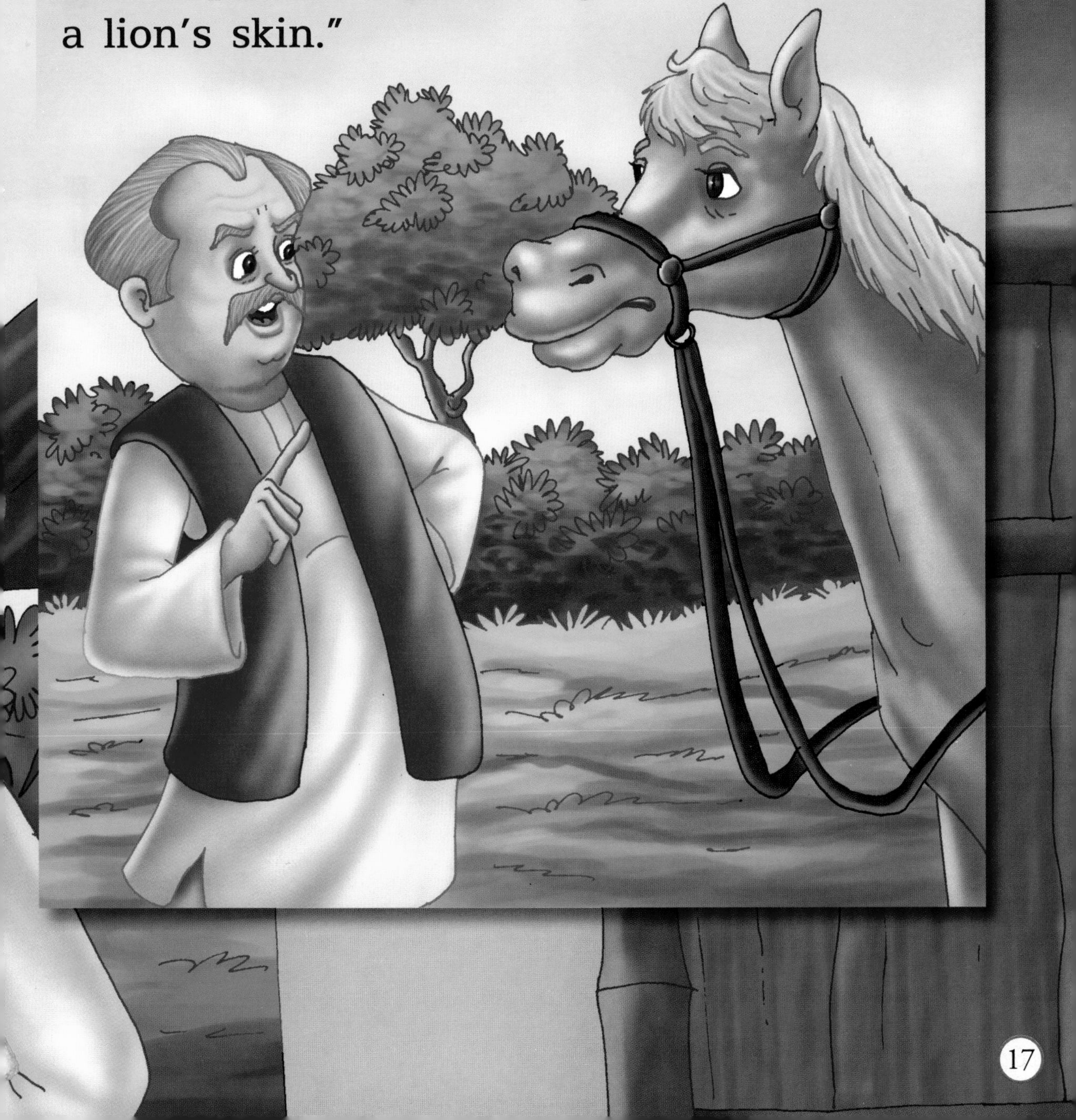

The horse was very disheartened at this answer, but he set out for the forest. He knew that it was a very difficult task and he would not be able to do it.

He reached the forest where he met a fox. The fox was smart and wise. They became friends. The horse told the fox about his story. She took pity on the horse and assured him that she would think of a plan to overcome his problem.

Very soon, she had a brilliant idea. There was a cruel lion in that forest. He was the king and all the animals used to live in fear of him. The fox asked the horse to lie down on the ground and pretend that he was dead.

Then she went to the lion and told him, "Your Majesty, there is a dead horse in the forest. It is my duty to inform you. I will take you to that place." The lion was happy to hear that, and he followed the fox.

On reaching the spot, the fox said, "Let us pull this dead horse behind the bushes so that you can have a peaceful meal. I will tie his tail to yours so that we can easily drag him behind." The lion agreed without a question.

Instead of tying the tail, the clever fox tied the lion's leg with the horse's tail. She then asked the horse to run at top speed till he reached his master's house. The horse started running as fast as he could.

The lion could not do a thing except roar and cry with pain. He was dragged like a dead animal. He was slammed against many rocks and stones. He was wounded all over and started bleeding. By the time the horse reached his master's house, the lion was dead.

The farmer was shocked to see the dead lion with the horse. He had not expected the old horse to be successful. He was very happy to see the horse's loyalty. He said, "My dear friend, you can really do anything for me. You will live with me forever."

Three Fish in the Pond

Long ago, there was a big pond in a forest. There used to live many fish, frogs, and other water creatures in that pond. Among these creatures, there were three fish who were very good friends.

Out of these three fish, the eldest one had a family. She was wise and practical. She always used to give advice to the other two fish. She used to tell them many good things about life.

Out of the other two fish, one was very smart and intelligent. But the other, the youngest one, was very lazy. She did not like to work at all. She had a negative attitude towards life.

One day, all three were sitting and chatting. Suddenly, a frog came hurriedly and said, "Run, my dear friends, run. The fishermen will catch you all. Just save your life and run from here." The eldest fish asked him calmly, "What has happened, dear frog? Tell us clearly."

He narrated the whole incident to them, "Listen friends, I was sitting on the ground near the pond. I saw three fishermen passing by. They stopped near the pond and were talking to each other, saying that they would come tomorrow with a net and catch you all."

On hearing this, all the fish were frightened. The eldest one said, "Do not worry, friends. We can go to the nearby pond for our safety. We will come back once the fishermen leave."

Most of the fish agreed to this suggestion except for some, including the eldest fish's two friends.

They said, "Why should we run like cowards from this pond? Let the fishermen come. Besides, who knows if the fishermen would really turn up here. After all, everyone has to die one day. So why be afraid of death?"

The eldest fish tried to convince them that it was not wise to stay in the pond and take such a risk when they were already warned of the coming danger. But they chose not to move out of the pond. The eldest fish sadly left the pond with her family.

The next morning, the fishermen came with a very big net. They spread their net in the pond. These two fish along with some others were caught in the net. They tried to escape, but it was of no use.

The youngest one started crying. The other one was still hopeful, as she was intelligent and smart. She acted very quickly and folded her body in an abnormal way, pretending that she was dead of some disease.

When the fishermen were checking all the fish, one of them noticed her and said, "Hey friends, see this fish is dead of some disease. It is of no use to us." He threw the fish back in the water.

In this way, the smart fish was saved because of her presence of mind. The youngest one, who was lazy and a pessimist, ended her life with her own hands.

The Rooster and the Fox

There was a cunning fox in a forest. Once, he was wandering in the forest to find his meal. Suddenly, he saw a fine, plump rooster sitting on the branch of a very high tree, looking at the dense forest around him.

The fox knew that he could not climb up the tree to kill the rooster, and so he wondered, *How can I get this rooster for my meal? If I just ask him to come down, he won't trust my intentions.*

The fox thought of a trick. He cunningly said to the rooster, "Dear friend, why are you sitting so high on the tree? Are you scared of somebody? Do you not know what the king of the forest has decided in a meeting of animals today?"

The rooster said innocently, "No, I have no idea of that. Please tell me the king's decision." The fox continued, "The decision is that from now onwards, animals and birds will not kill each other for food. Bigger fish will not eat smaller fish."

The rooster felt that something was very wrong. This couldn't be true. He asked, "Does that mean the lions, tigers, and leopards will

start eating grass from today?" The fox had no answer for this. But he did not want to give up so easily.

He said, "I can see you are not convinced. Come down, let us go to the king and ask for the clarification of this point. He will definitely answer our queries. After all, he has decided this for the betterment of everyone."

The rooster was smart enough to understand the fox's trick. He said, "You are right, we should go to the king for clarification. Why do we not take along some more friends with us? It will be better if more and more animals come to know about this decision."

Thinking that he had succeeded in his trick, the fox said, "Yes, yes, why not? We can take some more animals along. But first, you come down, then we can look for them." The fox was expecting the rooster to come down. He was thrilled.

Suddenly, the rooster said, “We are lucky, we don’t have to look for other friends. I can see some of your friends are just coming to this side. They are about to reach this place. We can take them along.”

The fox said, "Oh, that is good! But who are these animals?"

The rooster replied, “I can see a big group of hounds coming this way. I hope they are great friends with you?”

“Hounds!” the fox shouted in panic. He started running for dear life. The rooster asked, "Why are you running now? You have just told me that all the animals and birds have become friends with each other.”

The fox replied, “But perhaps the hounds might not have heard of this decision.” He ran away into the deep forest. The rooster laughed at the fox’s foolish idea. All the birds sitting on the tree cheered the rooster’s wit.

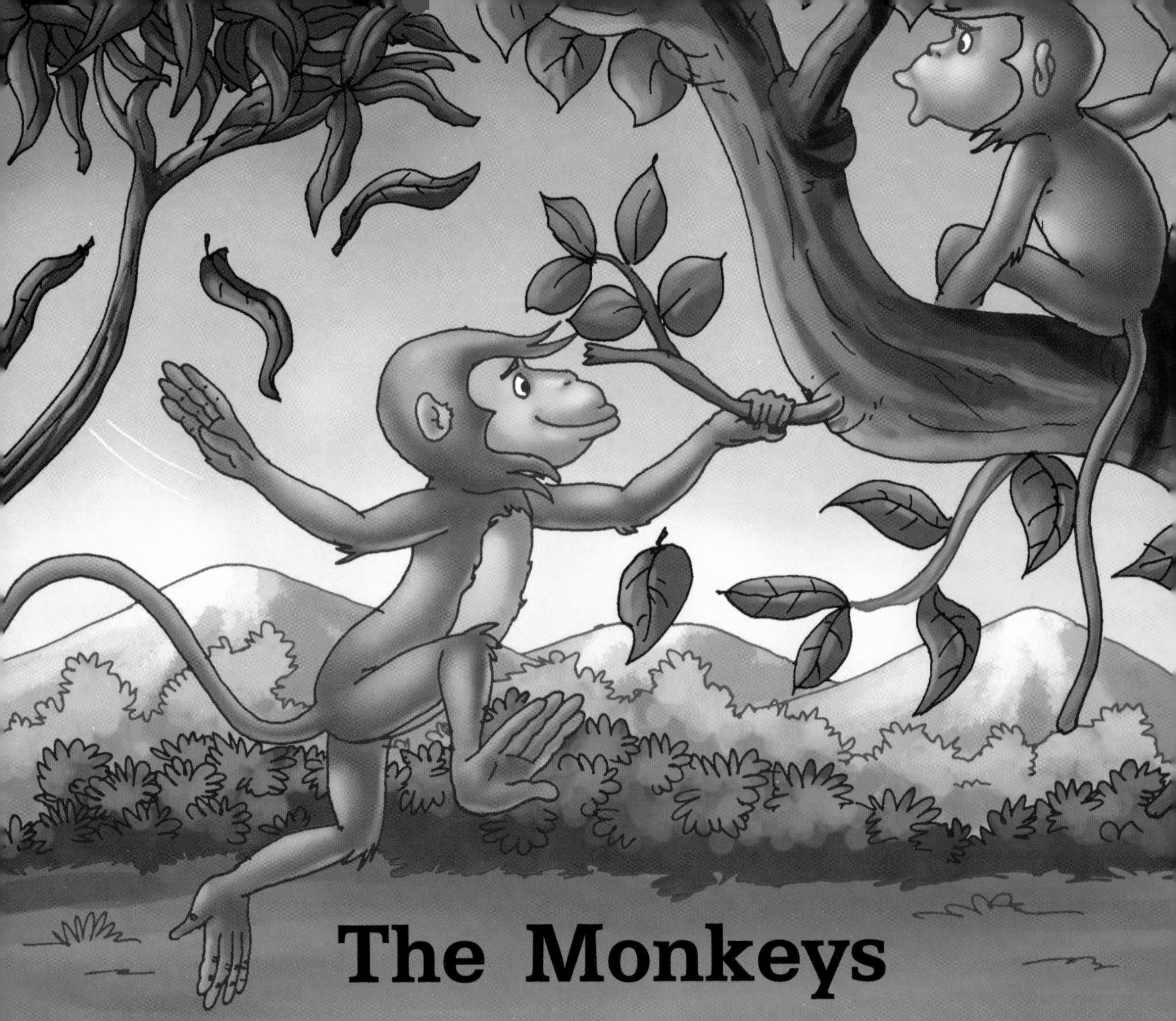

The Monkeys and the Red Berries

Long ago, there was a very large group of monkeys in a hilly region. They were very mischievous. They used to jump from one tree to another and would snatch things from the hands of the people in that area.

They even tore barks and leaves of trees and sometimes, fought with each other over little things. In fact, they thought themselves to be the wisest animals and hardly used their brains in anything.

Once there was a severe cold in that hilly area. All the monkeys began to shiver from the cold. They could not find any place to protect themselves.

One of the monkeys suggested to the others, "Friends, we should move to some other place to save ourselves from this cold. If we stay here for some more time, we will die."

All the monkeys agreed to his suggestion and they shifted from the hilly area to a nearby village. From the very next day, they again started their silly activities.

Instead of staying calmly in that village, they started teasing the families living there, got inside their houses, and spoiled many things in the village.

The villagers were so angry that together they hit them with stones and sticks, and cursing all the while, they threw the mischief-making monkeys out of their village.

Since now the monkeys had nowhere to go, they had to come back to the hilly area. By this time, the hilly area had become colder and chilly winds had begun to blow.

They saw some villagers lighting a fire and sitting around it. They saw some red balls, which were actually coal, burning below the wood sticks.

They gathered the wooden sticks but could not understand what the red balls were. They looked everywhere and found some red berries on a tree. They thought these were the same red balls.

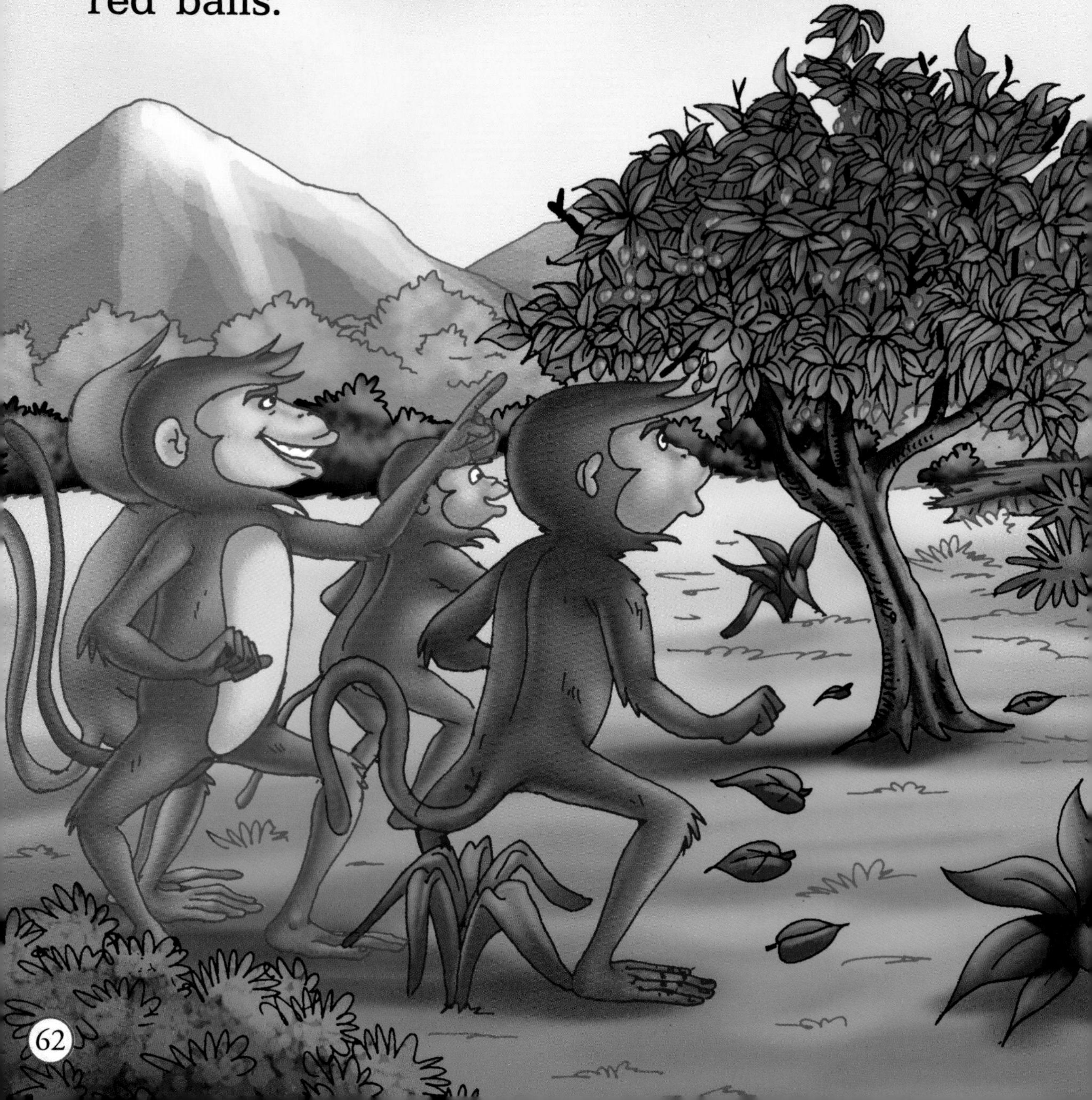

They plucked the berries and put them below the wooden sticks. They tried to make a fire by blowing into the pile. But there was no fire. The monkeys became very sad and disappointed with their failure.

There were also a few birds that lived in the same tree where the monkeys lived.

Seeing the plight of the monkeys, one of the birds said to them, "Friends, what are you doing? You are trying to make fire from red berries.

Have fruits ever made fire? Why do all of you not take shelter in the nearby cave?"

When the monkeys saw the little bird advicing them, they became red with rage. One old monkey said, "How dare you advice us! We are intelligent creatures."

And with that, the monkeys started throwing the berries at the birds, trying to drive them away. The birds that were trying to help them, decided to fly away, realising there was no use advicing fools.

The Talking Cave

Long ago, there lived a lion. He was old and not very strong anymore. Once, he did not get any prey for two days. He tried to look for food everywhere but could not find a thing. He became very weak.

One day, while he was wandering in the jungle hopelessly, he came across a cave. He thought, "There must be some animal inside this cave. I will hide myself behind the bushes. When the occupant comes out, I will eat it."

He hid behind the bushes. He waited for many hours but nobody came out of the cave. He was starving terribly and got irritated. Suddenly he thought, “Maybe the occupant is somewhere out in the jungle. I should wait inside the cave, not outside.”

Looking around the cave, the lion stealthily got inside, thinking, "Now, this is a good idea. I will pounce on the animal as soon as it enters the cave." Again he waited for hours but there was no one. He was losing his patience.

After some time, a fox came near the cave. The cave belonged to her. The fox was very smart. She was living in that cave for a very long time and was familiar with the surroundings of the cave. She felt that something was definitely wrong.

She was walking very slowly and silently towards the cave. Suddenly, she noticed the pugmarks of a lion going towards the cave and thought, "It looks like a lion has entered my cave. How do I make sure if he is still inside, waiting?"

The fox used her presence of mind. She played a trick. She stood at some distance from the cave to save herself in case of a sudden attack and shouted, "Hello cave! I have come back. Why are you so silent today, my dear cave? May I come in and occupy my residence?"

On getting no answer, she again shouted, "Are you angry with me, dear cave? See, if you do not welcome me in the usual manner, I will go to some other cave. I will never come back to you again!"

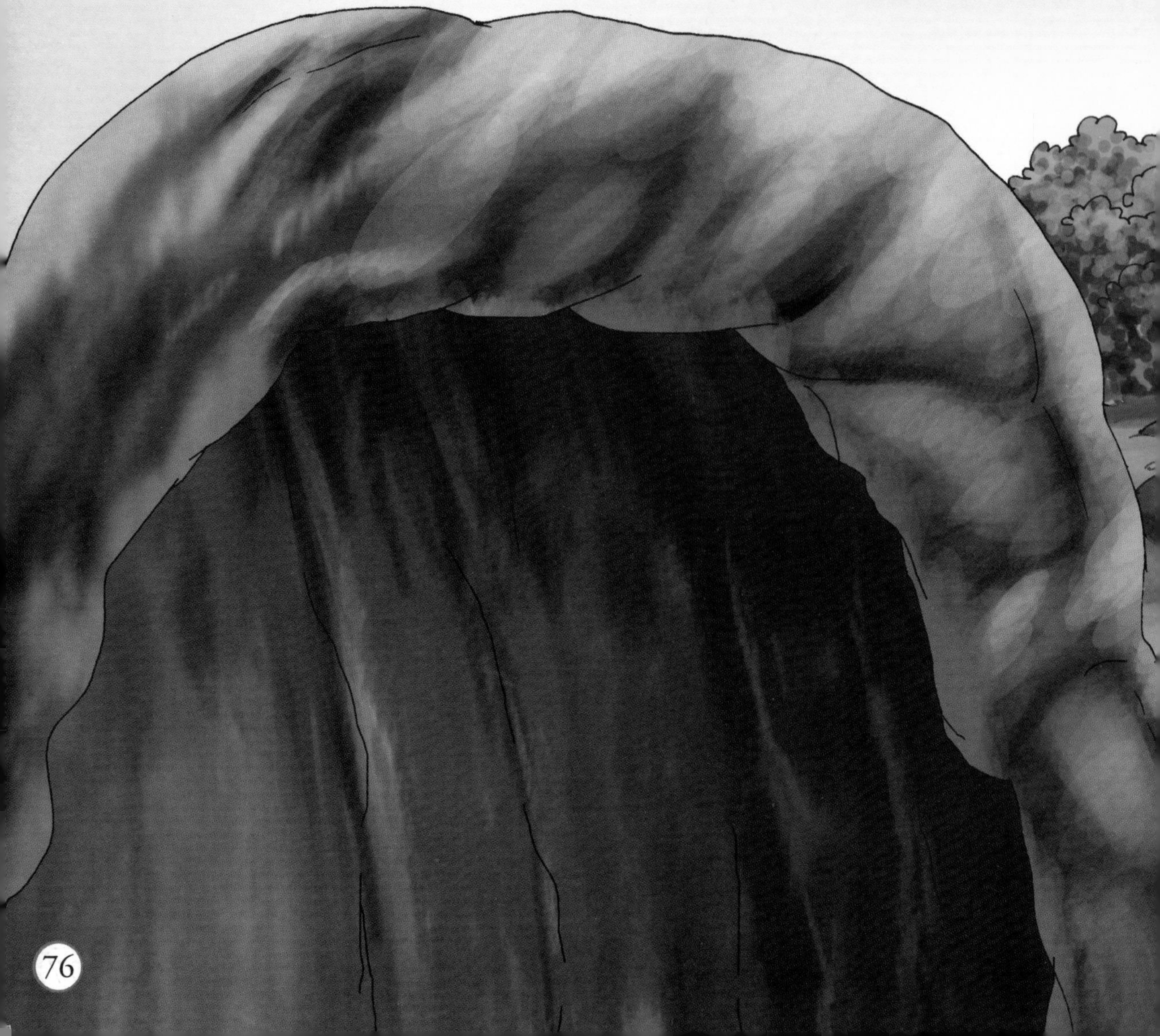

Hearing this, the lion thought, "Ah, the cave I am hiding in, must definitely be a talking cave! The cave is keeping quiet because of my presence inside. If the cave does not answer the fox's question, the fox will go away."

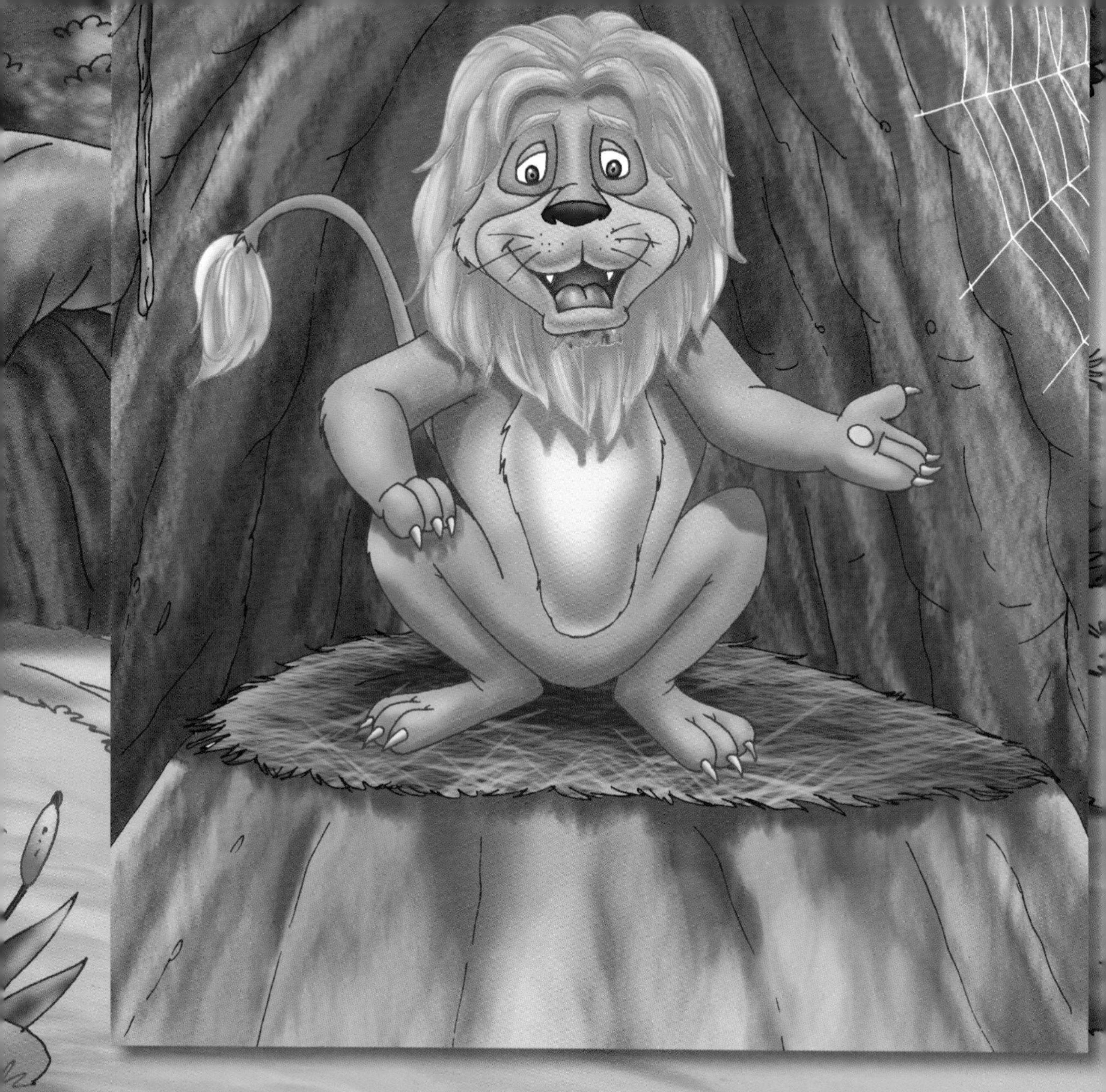

Thinking that he was very wise, the lion answered in a roaring voice on behalf of the cave, "I have not forgotten my practice of talking to you when you come, my dear fox. I slept so I could not hear your voice. Please come in."

And now, the clever fox was absolutely sure that a wicked lion was hiding in her cave. She ran away in a flash. She was happy with the trick she had played. While running, she laughed and said to herself, *Only a fool would believe that a cave can talk!*

OTHER TITLES IN THIS SERIES